# My Brother
# Is Not a Monster

*A Story of Addiction and Recovery*

*by* Lee S. Varon

*illustrated by* Alisha Monnin

Rachlee Books • Boston • USA

Rachlee Books
leesvaron@gmail.com
leesvaron.com

Printed and bound in the United States of America
First Edition

LCCN 2021921198

ISBN 979-8-9851363-0-2 (hc.)    ISBN 979-8-9851363-1-9 (pbk.)

book bridge press

This book was proudly produced by Book Bridge Press
www.bookbridgepress.com

This book is dedicated to all those who have been touched
by substance use disorder.
—L. V.

For my sister, who betters the lives of children every day.
—A. M.

## Acknowledgments

I want to give thanks to all my friends and family
who helped make this book a reality.
Although there are too many people to name here,
I would like to give thanks to David Rachlin, my partner and a clinical
social worker with years of experience helping people on their recovery
journeys; my sons, Jose Varon and Jude McElroy;
my daughter-in-law, Jenna McElroy; and Sophia Hasenfus,
who helped me every step of the way.

I am also grateful to members of my
Nar-Anon Family group for their wisdom and support:
Phyllis Ann B., Mary C., Mary Ellen D., Donna G., Felicia M.,
Pat M., Nancy M., Annette P., and many others.

And special thanks to Maryanne Frangules, Executive Director of MOAR
(Massachusetts Organization for Addiction Recovery)
and Julia W. Londergan, Esq., Director of Development CASPAR/
Bay Cove Human Services.
—L. V.

I was so excited! My brother Joey was going to take my best friend Casey and me trick-or-treating.

"I'm sorry I have to work at the hospital on Halloween, Sophia," Mom said. "But I'm happy Joey can go with you and Casey. Our neighborhood is the best for trick-or-treating."

Mom took Casey and me shopping that day for our Halloween costumes. I chose a superhero outfit and Casey picked a ninja costume. Then we went to look at a pair of butterfly earrings I've been saving my money to buy.

Joey was supposed to come shopping with us, but he never showed up. That made Mom angry. Joey's been missing a lot of family events lately. I'm worried he will forget about Halloween!

When we got home, Mom went upstairs to Joey's room. "Where were you?" she yelled. "You're being so selfish!"

Casey and I didn't want to hear them arguing, so we hung out in my room. I wanted to count the money I'd been saving for the butterfly earrings.

"My piggybank is empty!" I gasped.

"The money has to be there," Casey said. "I just counted it with you last week!"

"Mom!" I cried. "My piggybank's empty!"

Mom came into my room and I turned my piggybank upside down.

"Joey knew I was saving my money," I said. "He probably stole it all to buy his stupid cigarettes!"

Mom sighed. "Don't worry, honey. I'll take care of it."

"Joey doesn't even need a costume for Halloween!" I shouted. "He's a big old monster without one."

Joey wasn't always the kind of brother who would steal my money. He used to talk to me. I miss the old Joey. The old Joey gave me his peppermint ice cream cone after I dropped mine on the ground. The old Joey taught me how to pitch a softball and hit a home run. The old Joey brought home my pet bunny, Ronny.

But then Joey started staying out late and hanging out with a boy named Harry. They spent a lot of time in Joey's room. Once Mom smelled something funny coming from his room. She ran upstairs and pounded on the door.

"What do you want?" he shouted.

"I know you're smoking something! That's not allowed in this house!" Mom said loudly. When Joey finally opened the door, that funny-smelling smoke filled the hallway.

Joey didn't forget about Halloween after all! He painted his face white and colored some of his teeth black. He really looked like a monster!

I swished my red cape and Casey swung her sword. We were excited to start trick-or-treating.

"Come on, kids." Joey clapped his hands. "Let's get some candy!"

I told Joey a million times not to call me kid, but that night I didn't mind. I was just glad he was being nice again.

We marched along the streets, knocking on doors and shouting, "Trick or treat!" At one house, a witch answered the door and smiled at us. At another, fake cobwebs hung from the windows and a giant plastic spider dropped down when we rang the doorbell. Casey and I screamed and laughed.

Ghosts and zombies and pirates crowded the sidewalks. As our bags grew heavy with candy, Joey fell farther behind. I looked back and saw Harry walking beside Joey. They were smoking cigarettes.

After we knocked on a few more doors, Casey said,
"I don't see your brother. Isn't he supposed to be with
us?" She offered me a blue jellybean because she
knows they're my favorite.

I didn't see Joey anywhere, and I was a little worried.
Where did he go? I asked Casey if she wanted to
head back to my house to count our loot.

When we got home, I took the key from around my
neck and unlocked the front door. Joey's boots were
by the bottom of the stairs. I was angry he left us, so
I didn't even yell "Hi" upstairs.

Casey and I dumped our candy into piles. I counted
forty-two pieces. Casey had forty-three. I traded my
lollipops and licorice for her chocolate.

Suddenly, we heard a loud crash from Joey's room. Casey and I ran upstairs.

I knocked on his door and yelled, "Joey, what happened? Let me in!"

I tried the door and was surprised when it opened. Joey was lying on the floor. There was a sharp needle on the floor next to Joey like the ones the doctor uses to give shots.

"Get out of here," Joey said. "No babies allowed!" His monster face was still painted on. His words sounded slow and jumbled, like he was talking under water, and his head rolled forward.

"I'm not a baby!" I said. "Why do you sound funny?"

"Get out!" he mumbled.

"Why do you have that needle?" I asked.

Joey didn't say anything. He tried to stand up, but slumped down against the side of the bed. I screamed his name and shook him, but Joey didn't respond. His lips looked blue.

"We have to call someone!" Casey said. I grabbed her hand and rushed downstairs to call Mom.

Mom answered her phone right away.

"Mom, you need to come home! Joey's fallen on the floor, and I can't wake him up!"

"Oh no!" Mom said. "I'm calling 911 and coming right home!"

Casey held my hand while we waited. We were both scared.

Joey didn't answer when I asked about the needle, but I think I know what it was. Once on the playground at school, a kid found a needle just like it. Our teacher told us not to touch it, and she called the police. Later that day, the principal explained that the needle had probably been used by someone to take an illegal drug. "You all did the right thing when you called your teacher and made sure not to touch it," the principal said.

Mom was home soon, and I could hear a siren behind her. She hugged me and ran upstairs to Joey's room.

The ambulance arrived. "Follow me," I told the emergency medical technicians (EMTs), and we rushed upstairs.

The EMTs spoke loudly to Joey and rubbed his chest. Then one of them sprayed something into his nose. They called Joey's name loudly and kept rubbing his chest.

Mom held me close. I could feel her heart beating fast, and mine was too.

They gave Joey some more of the spray in his nose. I saw his chest rise and he coughed and muttered. He opened his eyes and sounded angry. "What's everyone doing? Get away from me!" Joey yelled.

One of the EMTs told Joey, "You overdosed. We gave you Narcan, a medicine to reverse the effects of the drugs you took. We need to take you to the hospital now."

"I don't want to go to a hospital," Joey mumbled. But the EMTs and Mom insisted, and they put him on a bed with wheels and brought him down the stairs.

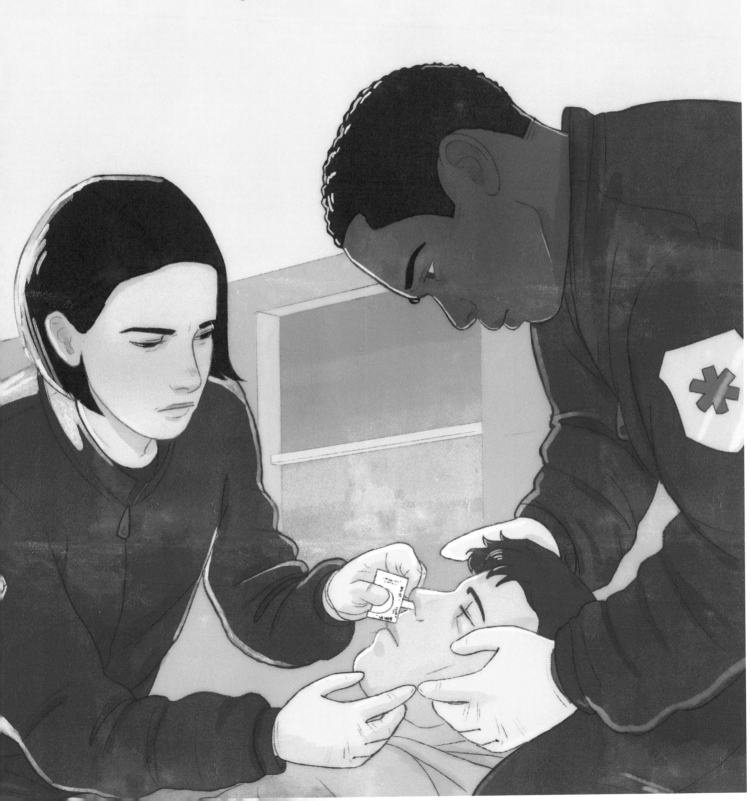

As they wheeled him outside to the ambulance, Joey looked confused and angry, but he didn't fight them anymore.

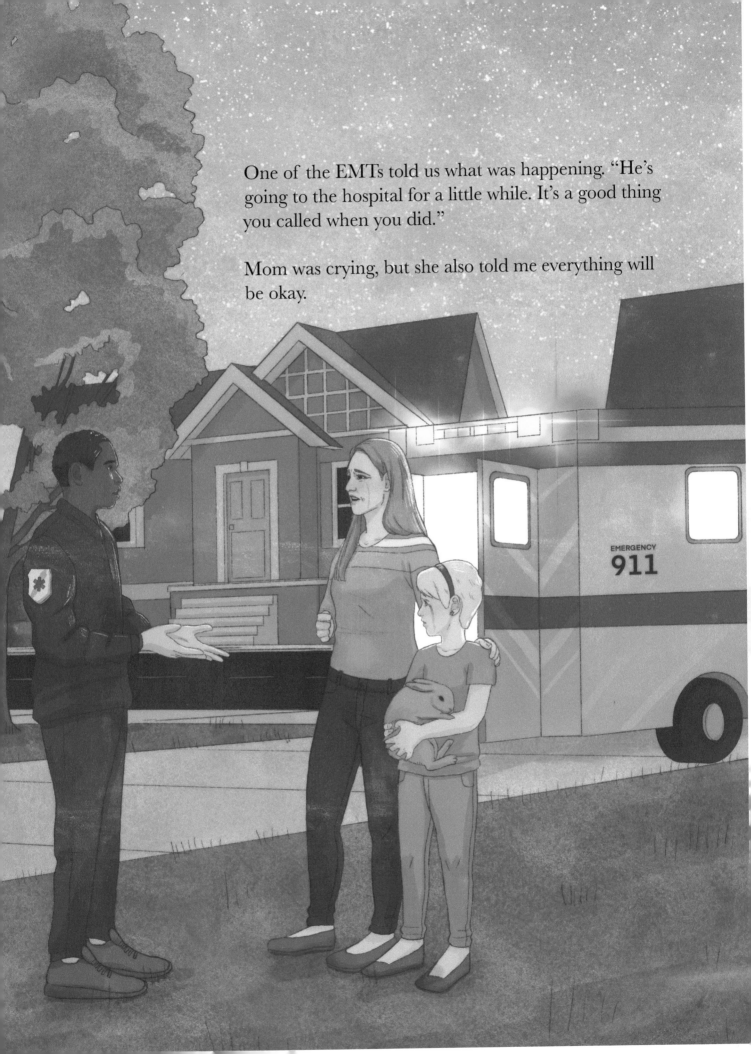

One of the EMTs told us what was happening. "He's going to the hospital for a little while. It's a good thing you called when you did."

Mom was crying, but she also told me everything will be okay.

I stayed with Casey and her parents that night so Mom could be with Joey at the hospital. The next day, Mom told me Joey was going to be okay, but that he took a drug called heroin that is very dangerous. "Sometimes people can die from it," Mom said. I asked her why people would take the drug if it's so dangerous.

"Joey has a disease called addiction," Mom said. "At first the drug might make someone feel good, but then they need to take more and more of it because they begin to feel sick without it. Sometimes they may do bad things to get money to buy drugs."

"I'm sorry I called Joey a monster," I said.

"It's okay," Mom said. "He was acting like a monster, like when he stole the money you were saving for your earrings."

After Joey was well enough to leave the hospital, he went to a special place called "rehab" to get help for his drug problem. Then after he came home, he started at a new school called a recovery high school. Everyone at his new school has the same disease as Joey. They're all trying to get better.

And Joey is getting better. I can tell. He's starting to make new friends. I asked him if he likes his new school. "I didn't want to go at first," he said. "But now I like it. Everyone is working to get better and stay away from drugs and alcohol. We support each other."

One night while I was doing my homework, Joey
knocked on my door. "Here," he said. He handed me
a small box. Inside were the blue and gold butterfly
earrings.

"Wow! Thanks, Joey," I said. "I love them." I jumped
up and gave him a big hug.

I feel like the monster is gone. I have my brother Joey
back again.

# Thoughts and Reflections

These pages are for you to think about, write about, or even draw about your feelings and experiences. Use a separate piece of paper or your own journal to write your thoughts and reflections.

*In the book, when Joey was using drugs, Sophia felt he was like a different person. "I miss the old Joey," she said. She felt her brother was different because he was missing family events, was often irritable, and did things like steal her money.*

Does the person you care about who is using drugs and/or alcohol act or seem different to you? How?

lonely

important

special

guilty

FED UP

fearful/scared

HURT

ANGRY/MAD

anxious

betrayed

hateful

DISAPPOINTED

INDIFFERENT

*In the book, Sophia called her brother Joey a monster when he was acting differently. She was angry when she thought he stole money from her piggy bank. She was upset that he disappeared with his friend when she and Casey went trick-or-treating with them.*

Feelings are not good or bad—they are just your feelings. Don't judge yourself for having feelings—even mad and angry feelings. Be kind to yourself and remember that it is completely normal to have many different feelings if someone you care about has substance use disorder (SUD), the proper term for addiction. Sometimes you have lots of feelings all at once.

You can even love and feel hate for someone at the same time. Sometimes you feel a lot of love for the person with substance use disorder at the same time that you feel angry and upset with the way the drugs or alcohol are making them act.

You might be feeling many feelings at once, and they are all valid and okay.

What feelings have you had about someone's substance use disorder?

JEALOUS
misunderstood
superior
ignored sad
scared
frustrated
ashamed
BRAVE
caring
compassionate
FRUSTRATED
OVERLOOKED
embarrassed
EXCITED
irritated
confused
NERVOUS
ashamed
different
flip

# More Thoughts and Reflections

Many people keep a journal or diary. A journal can help you sort out and understand your feelings and thoughts. Consider writing your feelings in a journal. Or you may want to take a selfie or draw a picture of how you feel. If you like music, you may express yourself by playing music or writing a song. It is helpful to have a way to express your feelings, so that they won't get bottled up inside of you. When this happens, it doesn't mean your feelings disappear. They may come out in unexpected ways like in a sudden outburst of anger or tears. Or they may come out in your body in the form of aches and pains, or extreme tiredness, or irritability.

When you have upsetting or uncomfortable feelings, what makes you feel better?

It sometimes helps to talk to someone you trust such as:

a parent/caregiver

a relative (grandparents, siblings, cousins, aunts, uncles, etc.)

a therapist

A COUNSELOR OR TEACHER AT SCHOOL

someone at your church, synagogue, or mosque

someone at a community center

a coach

ANOTHER ADULT YOU TRUST

Think of someone
you might be able to talk to about
how you are feeling.

# More Thoughts and Reflections

It's important to remember you didn't cause your loved one's problem, and it's not your job to fix them. You can't change them, but you can do things to make yourself feel better. Remember to treat yourself with kindness and compassion and do things that make you feel good. Don't forget to find things you like about yourself. Treat yourself the way you would treat your best friend.

Write five things that you like about yourself.

*In the book, Sophia's rabbit Ronny is often with her. It seems to help make her feel better and comforted.*

Some things to do that might make you feel better when you are upset include:

playing with a pet

spending time outside and/or in nature

EXERCISING OR PLAYING SPORTS

playing a board game or video game

spending time or playing with someone you have fun with

cooking a special dish

listening to music

READING A BOOK

starting a new hobby or project

joining a group for young people who have a family member or friend with substance use disorder (SUD)

# Write five things that make you feel better when you're feeling upset.

Another thing that might help you feel better is writing a letter to the person with substance use disorder, or to your parent/caregivers. It can help to write a letter even if you choose not to send it. This can help you think about what you might want to say. You may even want to write a letter of support to yourself.

*Sophia's mom gets angry and yells at Joey when he doesn't show up for Halloween shopping.*

Do you ever feel that someone's substance use disorder (SUD) affects other people in your family or other people you are close to? How?

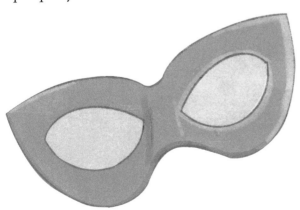

Sometimes adults or other members in a family affected by someone with substance use disorder (SUD) might even get angry at you, even though you did nothing wrong, instead of being angry at the person using drugs or alcohol. They may be irritable or preoccupied. It may not mean they are mad at you—they may be mad at the situation. But even if you know that, it can still be hard.

Has this ever happened to you?

*In the book, Sophia's friend Casey looks scared and says, "We have to call someone!"*

How do you think you would feel if you were Casey? What do you think you might do in her situation?

# More Thoughts and Reflections

*In the book, Sophia calls her mom when Joey is not waking up.*

What would you do if you found someone passed out or unresponsive like Joey was?

## Do you have a plan?

## WHAT DOES IT INCLUDE?

Ask your parent, caregiver, or someone you trust to help you write a list of who to call and what to do if you find someone passed out and unresponsive, or if you need help in any situation that might be scary.

*In the book, Sophia is very excited at the end after Joey completes treatment at a rehab center and goes to a recovery high school. She feels she has the old Joey back again.*

If someone you love has received treatment and is better, you may be very excited. You may also still be anxious and scared, and worry that the person might go back to the way they were in the past. It is very normal to feel this way, and it can take a long time to trust someone again.

Even if your loved one does start using drugs and/or alcohol again, it doesn't mean they won't get help another time. As hard as it may be, remember that no matter what they do, you can still take care of yourself and have a happy life.

# A Note from the Author

Most people with substance use disorder have families. Many of these families have children like Sophia. These children often feel alone, confused, angry, sad, and frightened as they watch their family member struggle with this disease.

It is important that these young people and their families know they are not alone, that their feelings are normal, and that help is available.

According to the Centers for Disease Control and Prevention National Center for Health Statistics, drug overdose deaths in the United States soared to a record 93,000 for the year ending December 2020. About two-thirds of those deaths were related to opioids. But deaths due to cocaine and methamphetamine use have also been rising.

Many of these deaths could have been prevented if Narcan had been administered.

My hope in writing this book is that it will help raise awareness about substance use disorder for both children and their families. I also hope to provide education regarding the availability and use of Narcan, hopefully saving the lives of people who, like Joey, can get help for their disease and go on to live happy and productive lives.

Narcan nasal spray is easily administered. It has no major side effects. It can be obtained in every state and in many drugstores without a prescription. It is covered by most public and private insurances and often can be obtained free of cost.

If you or anyone you know is struggling with a substance use disorder, you should have Narcan in your home and know how to use it.

# Resources and Tips

## Tips for Parents/Caregivers

- Educate yourself about substance use disorder (SUD), the proper term for addiction.

- Educate yourself about the different options for help with SUD. These may include inpatient and outpatient treatment, as well as mutual aid groups. A few of these include detoxification (detox), individual and/or group therapy and counseling, faith-based programs, pharmacotherapy (previously called medication-assisted treatment), which includes medication for opioid use disorder (MOUD), 12-step meetings, SMART Recovery meetings, relapse prevention techniques, mindfulness, and many others. Many treatment programs include a combination of these modalities.

- Keep all medications in your home in a safe and secure place, and properly dispose of them when they are expired or no longer needed. Some young people may begin experimenting with drugs when they find prescription medications at home.

- Know the signs and symptoms of someone who is misusing opioids, other drugs, or alcohol.

- Keep a list of emergency contacts by the phone and make sure your children know whom to call and what to say if they need to make an emergency call. Role-playing these situations with children is often helpful.

- Know the signs of an overdose and how to respond to one. This includes calling 911, administering Narcan (more than one dose may be needed), and supporting the person's breathing (this may include rescue breathing).
Note: since Narcan can only reverse an overdose for 30 to 90 minutes, it is still important to get medical care.

## Tips for Young People

- You are not alone. Millions of kids like you have a relative or a friend who is struggling with drug or alcohol use.

- It is important that you don't keep your feelings bottled up inside.

- It is helpful to have a trusted individual to talk to. This may be your parent or caregiver, or it could also be a teacher or counselor at school, a clergy member, someone at a community organization, or another adult you trust.

- Your loved one may act irritable or even mean when they are struggling with substance use disorder (SUD), the proper term for addiction. That doesn't mean they don't love you.

- In this story, Sophia called her mom when Joey was unresponsive. It's important to know whom to call in case of an emergency. If you don't get ahold of an adult, call 911.

- Remember, there is treatment for people dealing with substance use disorder (SUD). People can get better. There is help available and there are many different ways to get well.

- Even if your loved one starts using drugs or alcohol again, this doesn't mean they can't get well. For some people it takes several attempts before they get better.

- Above all, remember that you did not cause your loved one's SUD.

It is helpful to think about these three points, often called the three C's (borrowed from 12-step programs):

1. You didn't **Cause** it. You did not cause your loved one's drug or alcohol problem.

2. You can't **Control** it. As much as you would like to, you cannot control your loved one's disease.

3. You can't **Cure** it. You cannot cure your loved one's disease.

## Resources

### Disclaimer

This is not an exhaustive list. Different things work for different people. It is often important to seek professional help when dealing with a loved one's SUD. Many of these resources may be helpful for both adults and children.

- **ASAM: American Society of Addiction Medicine**
  Medical society of physicians, clinicians, and associated professionals in the field of addiction medicine.
  301-656-3920
  asam.org

- **Faces & Voices of Recovery**
  Information and advocacy group dedicated to organizing and mobilizing Americans in recovery from addiction to alcohol and other drugs, as well as their families, friends, and allies. Works to eliminate stigma and demonstrate the power of long-term recovery.
  202-737-0690
  facesandvoicesofrecovery.org

- **NACoA: National Association for Children of Addiction**
  NACoA seeks to eliminate the adverse impact of alcohol and drug use on children and families.
  888-554-COAS (2627) or 301-468-0985
  nacoa.org

- **Partnership to End Addiction**
  An organization that runs campaigns to prevent teenage drug and alcohol use.
  drugfree.org
  Text the word "connect" to 55753, or visit the website to schedule a phone call or email a specialist.

- **SAFE (Stop the Addiction Fatality Epidemic) Project**
  The SAFE Project is a national nonprofit working to support an end to the opioid epidemic. To find out if Narcan is available in your state and how to obtain it, contact the SAFE Project:
  703-216-9633
  safeproject.us
  State-by-state rules:
  safeproject.us/naloxone-awareness-project/state-rules/

- **SAMHSA: Substance Abuse and Mental Health Services Administration**
  A federal agency whose mission is to reduce the impact of substance abuse and mental illness on America's communities. SAMHSA provides treatment, referrals, and information services (in English and Spanish) for individuals and families.
  Their website includes five steps to respond to an overdose in their Opioid Overdose Prevention Toolkit.
  SAMHSA's National Helpline:
  800-662-HELP(4357)
  samhsa.gov

- **USA.gov Mental Health & Substance Abuse**
  Mental health and drug and alcohol addiction treatment resources:
  usa.gov/mental-health-substance-abuse

# Mutual Aid Groups for Friends and Families

In many mutual aid groups, there are specialized meetings for individuals of any identity, including but not limited to LGBTQIA+, BIPOC, API, neurodiversity, ability, and gender. Check their websites for details.

## 12-Step Based

- **Adult Children of Alcoholics**
  Support for individuals who desire to recover from the effects of growing up in an alcoholic or otherwise dysfunctional family.
  310-534-1815
  adultchildren.org

- **Al-Anon Family Groups**
  A mutual support program for people whose lives have been affected by someone else's drinking. The 12 steps of Al-Anon are adapted from the 12 steps of Alcoholics Anonymous (AA). Although Al-Anon primarily began for people affected by someone else's drinking, increasingly people who are affected by someone else's drug use attend meetings.
  888-425-2666
  al-anon.org

- **Alateen**
  A part of Al-Anon Family Groups. A fellowship for young people whose lives have been affected by someone else's drinking or drug use.
  al-anon.org

- **Families Anonymous (FA)**
  FA is a 12-step fellowship for families and friends of individuals with drug, alcohol, or related behavioral issues.
  800-736-9805
  familiesanonymous.org

- **Nar-Anon Family Groups**
  A 12-step fellowship for families and friends of those with SUD (primarily drugs).
  800-477-6291
  nar-anon.org

- **Narateen**
  A part of the worldwide fellowship of Nar-Anon Family Groups for young people whose lives have been affected by a relative or friend's SUD.
  800-477-6291
  nar-anon.org/narateen

## Primarily Non-12-Step

- **Grief Recovery After Substance Passing**
  GRASP is a community designed to support people who have lost someone they love to addiction and overdose.
  grasphelp.org

- **LifeRing Secular Recovery**
  LSR is a secular nonprofit that provides peer-run addiction recovery groups. It also assists partners, family members, and friends of those struggling with alcohol and SUD.
  lifering.org

- **Parents of Addicted Loved Ones**
  PAL is a Christian-run nonprofit based on one founding phrase: "People helping people through the woods." PAL meetings are usually run weekly and provide support for parents who have children who are addicted to drugs or alcohol.
  480-300-4712
  palgroup.org

- **Recovery Dharma**
  Peer-led movement and community. The program uses the Buddhist practice of meditation, self-inquiry, wisdom, compassion, and community as tools for recovery and healing. Some of the meetings are open to friends and family.
  recoverydharma.org

- **SMART Recovery Family & Friends**
  A science-based program for family members of people living with addiction. SMART Recovery Family & Friends has meetings in many cities.
  440-951-5357
  smartrecovery.org

- There are many online/social media–based support groups. One of the largest is The Addict's Mom at theaddictsmom.com.
  Its credo is "sharing without shame." There are over 25,000 members with chapters in every state.

# Glossary

### Addiction

The proper term for addiction is substance use disorder (SUD), further defined in this glossary.

### Fentanyl/Carfentanil

Synthetic opioids that are many times stronger than heroin.

### Good Samaritan Laws

Good Samaritan drug overdose laws provide immunity from legal consequences for possession of drugs or drug paraphernalia when individuals who are experiencing or witnessing an overdose summon emergency services. Good Samaritan Laws vary by state. Please check on the updated laws in your state.

### Harm Reduction

There are many definitions of harm reduction, but it is essentially a practical strategy to protect the individual, family, and community from the consequences of substance use.

Narcan is one type of harm reduction. Other methods of harm reduction include clean needles, first aid kits, and fentanyl test strips, which can identify the presence of fentanyl in unregulated drugs.

### Heroin

A powerful opioid obtained illegally (not with a doctor's prescription) used for its euphoric effects. It can cause respiratory depression and impaired mental functioning and can lead to addiction, overdose, and even death. Heroin is sometimes adulterated (mixed) with fentanyl, carfentanil, or other dangerous substances that make it much more potent and greatly increase the risk of overdose.

### Narcan

Narcan is the most common brand name for naloxone. Naloxone is the generic name for the opioid reversal medication, a legal medication used to block the effects of opioids. Narcan can reverse an opioid overdose. This is the medicine the EMTs gave Joey in the story. Adults can obtain Narcan and anyone, including children, can learn how to use it. Narcan is most commonly available as a nasal spray, but it can also be administered through injection. Narcan nasal spray is easily administered. It has no major side effects. If you or anyone you know is struggling with

substance use disorder, you can learn how to use Narcan and keep it in your home. It is good to have several unexpired doses available.

**To find out if Narcan is available in your state and how to obtain it, contact the SAFE Project at 703-216-9633, or at safeproject.us. You can also check getnaloxonenow.org.**

## Opioid
A natural, semi-synthetic, or synthetic substance. Opioids include prescription medications used to treat pain, as well as illegal drugs such as heroin. Opioids produce narcotic effects including pain relief, sedation, and slowed breathing. They can also produce euphoria. A doctor may prescribe some FDA-approved opioids for medical use, but when opioids are misused, they can lead to addiction, overdose, and even death. Some commonly used medications when illegally obtained might be mixed with fentanyl or other dangerous substances that make them much more potent and greatly increases the risk of overdose.

## Recovery
A self-determined process of change through which individuals improve their health and wellness and strive to reach their full potential. In the recovery community, many people say there is much more to recovery than no longer using drugs or alcohol.

## Recovery colleges and universities
A growing number of colleges and universities offer resources and support for students with SUD. Collegiate Recovery Programs (CRP) vary by location but often offer sober housing, self-help programs, individual counseling, and sober events. collegiaterecovery.org
Recovery Research Institute: recoveryanswers.org

## Recovery high schools
Recovery high schools are public or private schools where students can earn a high school diploma while they are supported in their recovery from alcohol and drug use. Association of Recovery Schools: recoveryschools.org

## Rehab
Short for rehabilitation, rehab is a program where one can receive treatment for SUD, either at a residential facility or an outpatient program.

## Substance Use Disorder (SUD)
There are different definitions of SUD. Most professionals consider SUD a disease in which the individual compulsively seeks drugs/alcohol despite harmful and sometimes long-lasting consequences.

CPSIA information can be obtained
at www.ICGtesting.com
Printed in the USA
LVHW071924180322
713806LV00010B/276

9 789898 513 6302